MODERN TOSS VI

*from *hitflap*

by Jon Link and Mick Bunnage

Modern Toss: PO Box 386, Brighton, BN1 3SN, United Kingdom
email: info@moderntoss.com www.moderntoss.com
First printed up in the year of 2010
Printed by Lancing Press, West Sussex, UK

THE INVISIBLE ARSEHOLE

Mr Tourette

MASTER SIGNWRITER

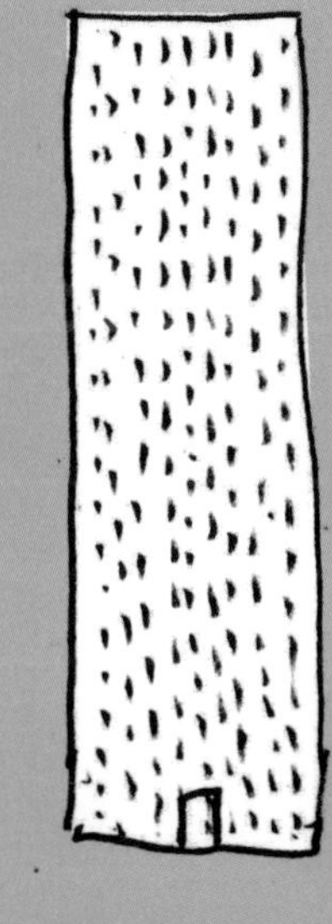

work

what are you like at multi-tasking?

pretty good, I often read the paper while I'm having a shit

fly talk

you still active on the old political scene?

yeah I've been hanging round with Gordon Brown lately, can get a bit intense. Me and the guys just tried to cheer him up with a little flying display over his desk, seemed to really set him off. He picked up a big leather chair and started roaring like a stag in the mirror, then he threw the chair at a filing cabinet. After that a woman came in and gave him a kit kat, seemed to calm him right down.

cheese&wine

enjoying the party Gerry?

yeah have you got a number for a prostitute?

Mr Tourette

MASTER SIGNWRITER

oh hello Mr Tourette I run me own local shop and want to start competing with the big boys on the food home delivery front

no problem i excel in helping people realise their last ditch, half-bollocked ideas just before their business goes up the shitter

Later...

nice one! just off on me first delivery, some bloke at the bottom of the road ordered a packet of cheese and onion crisps

you can't go wrong mate, its a full 'Mouse to Shitpan' service

TOTAL FUCKING DISASTER

in

'Sunday Roast'

home~clubber

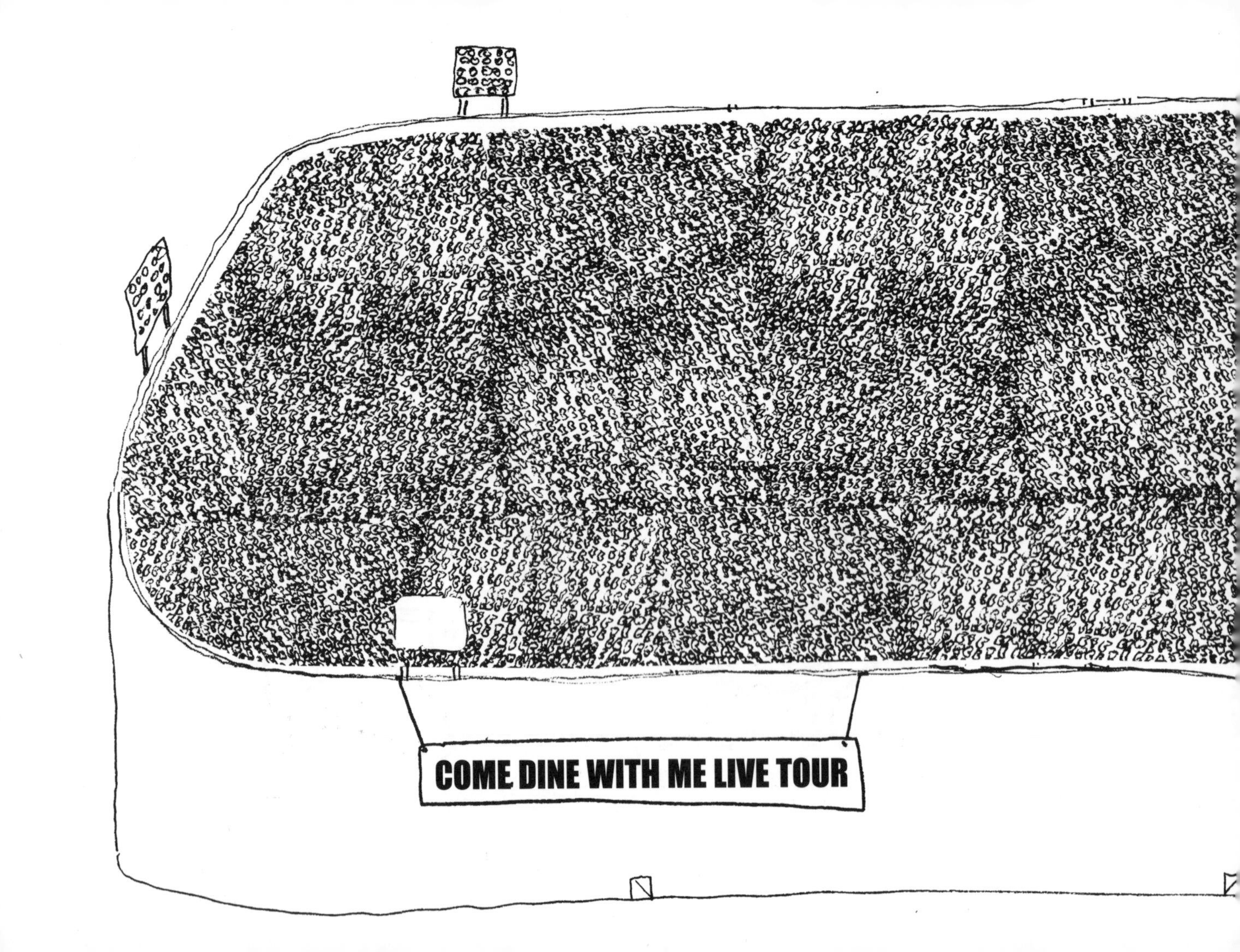
COME DINE WITH ME LIVE TOUR

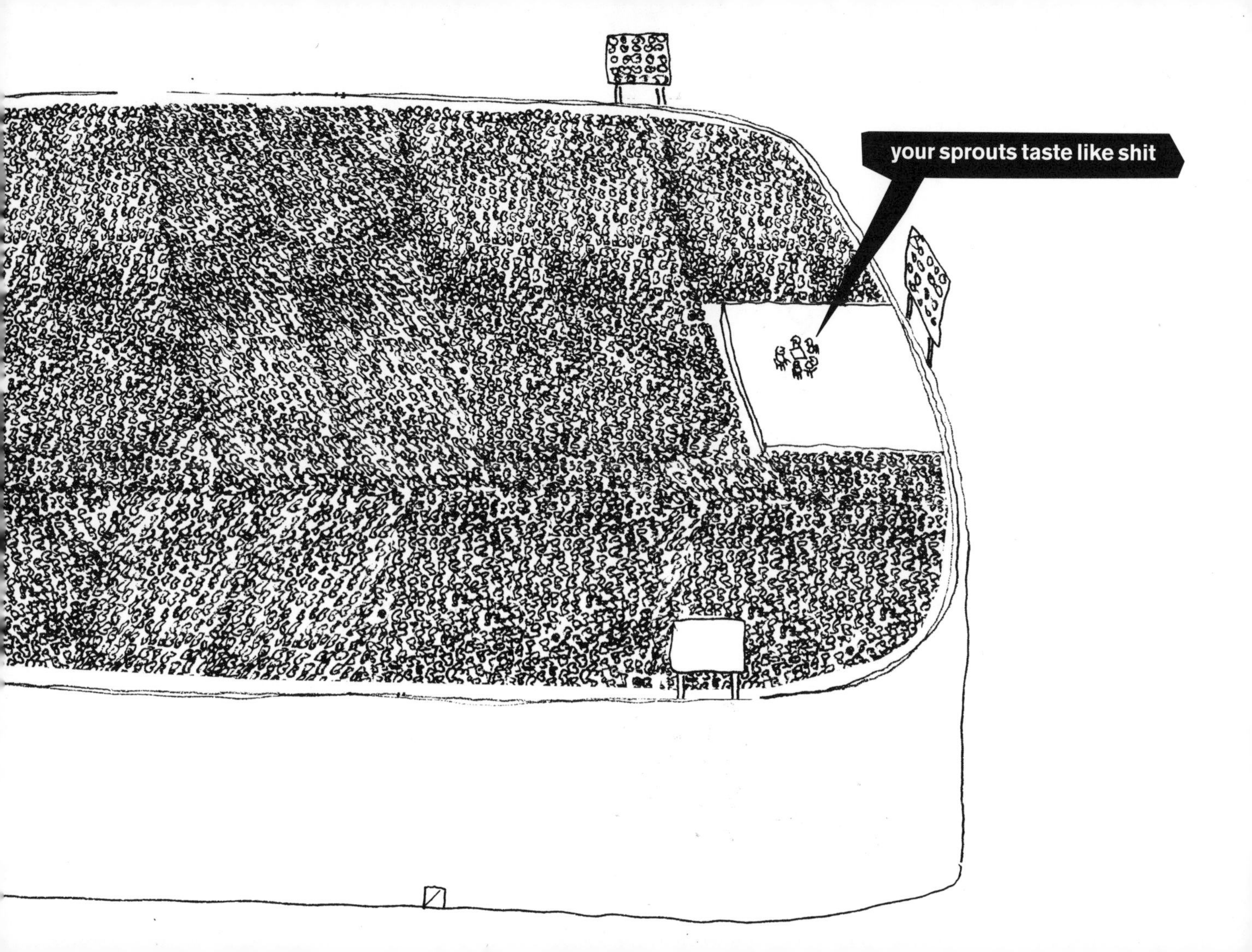
your sprouts taste like shit

drive-by abuser

considers 'The Newspaper Reader'

reading a newspaper?

catching up on the latest developments of all the shit that's going on?

I expect the world rests easier knowing you're up to speed with it all

I get it all online mate

not that i can be bothered most of the time

unless some footballer's fucked a prostitute or something

turns out they have, I'm off to check the latest see you around yeah!

BRITAINS GOT TALENT
what are you going to do for us today?
i was going to do a ventriloquist act, but i just bent down to do me shoelaces up and accidentally shit meself
it's a yes from me
you nailed it 1000%

Sorry To Hear About Your Loss

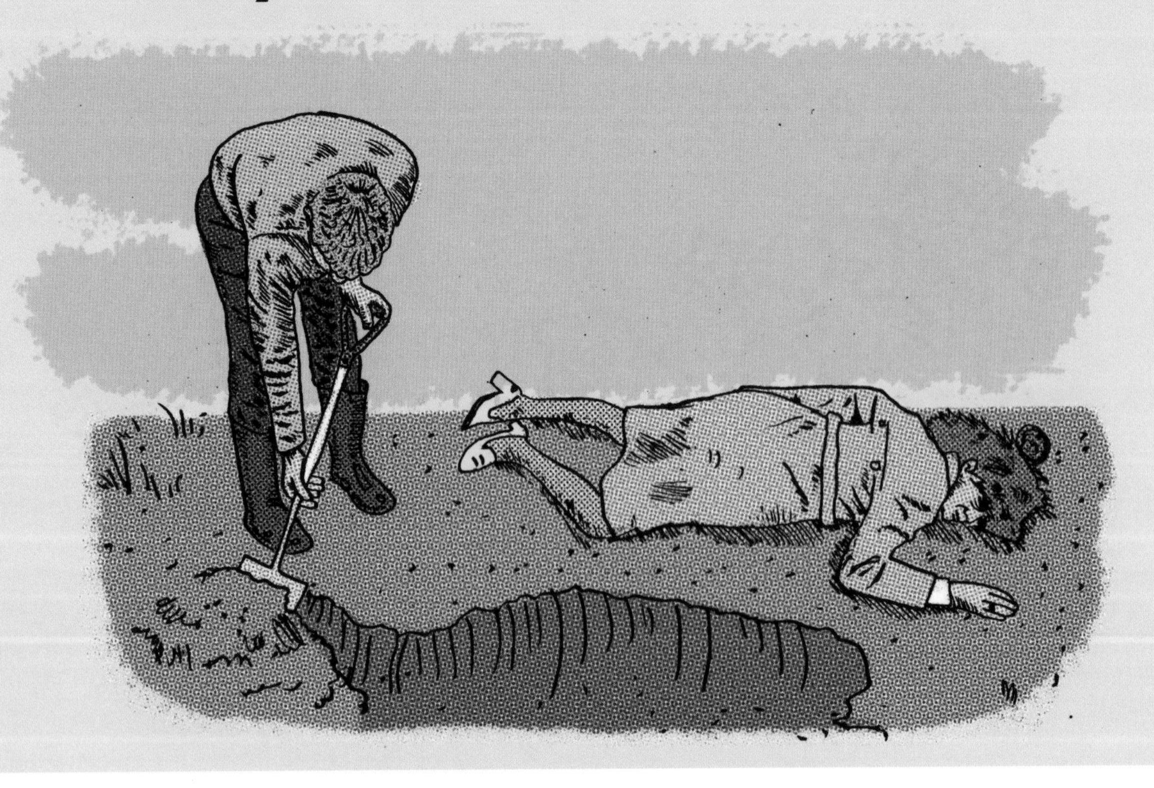

Experimental Greetings Card no1

Congratulations On Your Wife Becoming A Lesbian

Experimental Greetings Card no2

Pete Peters
Vigilante Shit Stirrer

consumer rights

PEANUT

HAVING SPLIT THE BAND AND RETREATED TO HIS TROUT FARM, GARY PREPARES TO EMBARK ON HIS MUCH-ANTICIPATED SOLO WORLD TOUR. FOR DAVE AND PAUL, THAT'S JUST ONE KICK IN THE NUTS TOO FAR...

OUTSIDE...
HERE COMES THE CUNT NOW
HERE COMES THE CUNT NOW
MORNING MR GARY, YOUR CAR IS READY
SEE YOU THEN
YEAH CHEERS SEE YOU
WHAT A FUCKING CUNT
WHAT D'YOU RECKON? FACE OR LIVER
TRY AND GET BOTH
BANG
SHITTER
UNGHARK.. IEEE

ARGHH FUCKING ARSEHOLES

CALL AN AMBULANCE MR GARY HAS BEEN SHOT
GARY 1
MR GARY DO YOU WANT ME TO CANCEL THE PRINTING OF THE WORLD TOUR PROGRAMME?

DON'T MOVE IT MIGHT BE LODGED IN YOUR SPINE
IT'S LIKE JOHN LENNON INNIT
THEY'VE SHOT ME RIGHT IN ME OWN TROUT FARM
DO YOU WANT A COFFEE OR SOMETHING?

THAT SHOULD PUT A STOP TO HIS WORLD TOUR AND DRIVE A LOT OF THE ORIGINAL PEANUT FANBASE TO OUR NEW SPLINTER GROUP WALNUT
YEAH, DO YOU THINK WE SHOULD SEND HIM A GET WELL CARD SO HE DOESN'T THINK IT WAS US?

MR GARY SOMEONE JUST RANG UP ABOUT RENEWING YOUR MOBILE PHONE CONTRACT, WHAT DO YOU WANT ME TO DO?
YEAH I NEED TO RENEW IT, ARGGH FUCK, YOU GOT THE NUMBER?
THEY DIDN'T LEAVE A NUMBER
PUNCH IN 1471, RETRIEVE IT YEAH, ARGHH
I'M NO EXPERT BUT ISN'T THAT HIS LIVER POKING OUT THERE?
TRY NOT TO TALK MR GARY, YOUR LIFE FORCE IS LOW

IN THE CARD SHOP
YEAH THAT'S A NICE ONE, BUT THE SENTIMENT'S ALL WRONG

OI MATE, YOU GOT ANYTHING FOR A BLOKE WHO'S BEEN SHOT IN THE LIVER?

AT THE HOSPITAL
OI SPODSIE, I THOUGHT WE PUT A NEWS BLACKOUT ON MY INJURY
WHAT YOU TALKING ABOUT YOU STUPID CUNT?
SOMETHING DOESN'T QUITE ADD UP, LISTEN TO THIS - 'SORRY TO HEAR ABOUT THAT BULLET IN YOUR LIVER, LOVE PAUL AND DAVE'
MORE BAD NEWS MR GARY, WE WERE HAVING A BIT OF A PARTY LAST NIGHT...

FOR FUCKS SAKE, I'VE ONLY BEEN IN HERE ONE NIGHT
SOMEONE KNOCKED AN ELECTRIC PATIO HEATER INTO THE LAKE, KILLING 50,000 TROUT INCLUDING YOUR TOP BREEDERS

FUCKING ARSEHOLES, IT CAN'T GET ANY WORSE CAN IT?

JUST BEEN CHECKING YOUR X-RAYS, WE GOT TO TAKE YOUR LIVER OUT, IF YOU DON'T GET A NEW ONE IN 24 HOURS YOU'RE DEAD YEAH

WHAT ABOUT A TROUT LIVER?
NO THAT WOULD NEVER WORK
NEVER SAY NEVER, I WANT THAT TROUT LIVER WHACKED INSIDE ME , IF I GET 10 MINUTES OUT OF IT, IT'LL HAVE BEEN WORTH IT
WE GOT 50,000 OF 'THE FUCKERS WE COULD JUST KEEP REPLACING THEM LIKE BATTERIES
TASTY, I'LL PR THE FUCK OUT OF IT, THIS COULD BE THE PRESS TEASER WE'RE LOOKING FOR TO LAUNCH THE NEW ALBUM
60 SECONDS LATER
CAN I JUST GET YOU TO SIGN THIS DISCLAIMER FORM, THIS ONES GOT A 98% CHANCE OF GOING TITS UP
IT'S ALL GOING DARK...

BLOG LAUREATE

thoughts to commemorate the recent football match between England and Kazakhstan

There's Rooney
strutting round majestically like a scouse swan ☻
His wife is watching admiringly from the stands,
As he coughs up an oyster on the hallowed turf
I bet he doesn't do that at home. ☻
She might fucking cheer up if he scores. LOL ☻

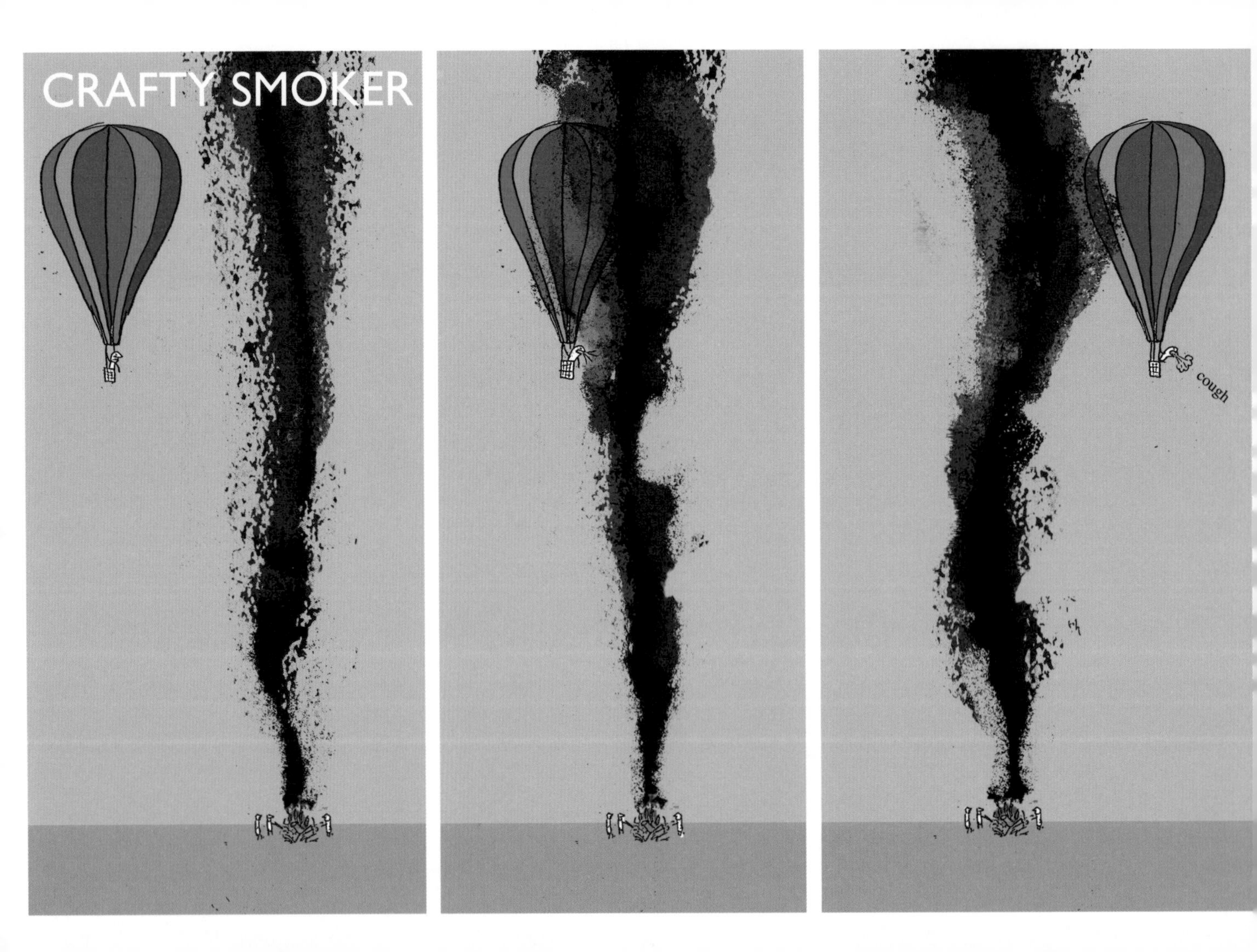
CRAFTY SMOKER
cough

skeleton in the cupboard

Mr Tourette

MASTER SIGNWRITER

hello Mr Tourette I need a sign for my budget meat supermarket, we are the first meat retailer to offer a whole chicken for 18 pence, it comes with anti-biotic stuffing in case it's got any residue bird flu in it

that's getting me mouth juices going already

LIBERTY TAKER

Retail village of the damned

work

how long have you worked here?

I don't work here, I'm trying to have a drink in the pub next door

Niche Obscenity Investigator

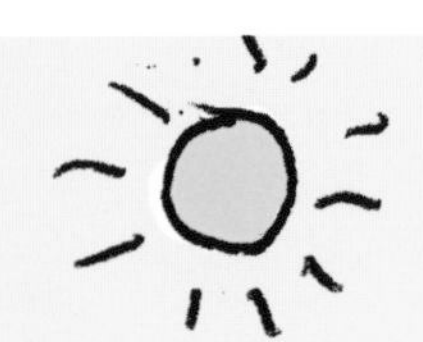

interview

alright if my mate films this in case you try and touch me up or anything

LIBERTY TAKER

oi mate out the way i want to test me new wrecking ball out on your house

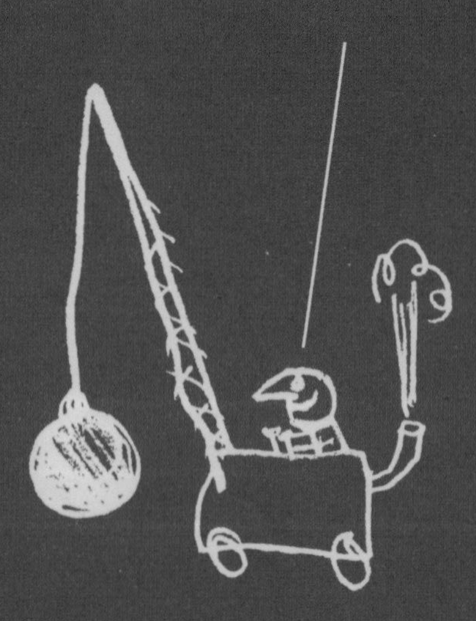

cheese&wine

is this the prostitute I ordered?
no this is my daughter Susan

interview

ahh now I see from your CV you've got tap dancing down as a hobby

yeah that's actually lap dancing, I can't type for shit

Pete Peters
Vigilante Shit Stirrer

EastEnders Nutshelled

dirty den's loophole

plot negotiations
My client agrees to do the 'nonce' storyline on condition he gets to clock Phil Mitchell one with an iron bar in the christmas special

publicity shoot
TV QUICK
ok Phil, I need you to do an expression that sums up the episode where you go ballistic with a handgun, hijack a Vauxhall Astra and drive it high speed into the River Thames
that's good, I like what you're doing with the eyebrow

emergency edit
bad news, we're coming up 10 minutes short on Thursday's episode.
Phil's offered to cover the bulk of it with a long sigh. he reckons he can string it out for two minutes if he rolls his eyes and looks around a lot

beale's moustache crisis meeting
a lot of viewers have complained that it's been putting them off their dinner
yeah it's actually making me feel a bit sick
I like it Ian, but frankly its a ratings disaster

Mr Tourette

MASTER SIGNWRITER

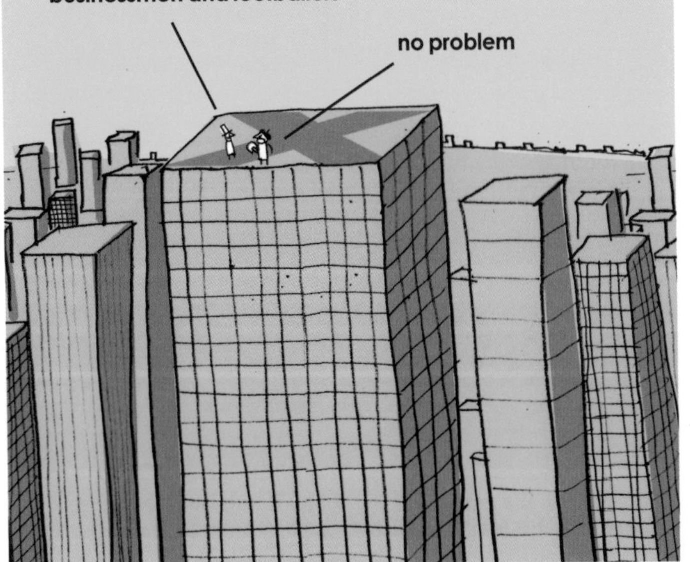

Later...

Pete Peters
Vigilante Shit Stirrer

home~clubber

legal longshots

Alan in "Arctic Cruise"
bloody hell Alan's cutting it a bit fine
we don't want him to miss the Arctic Cruise of a lifetime
it was his idea to come on it
here he comes now
bloody hell Alan nice luggage cart, I didn't know you were allowed to drive them on your own
you're not
and where is your luggage anyway?
I checked it in earlier, it was quite fucking bulky
excuse me sir we'd like a word with you

is this your luggage?
yeah what the fuck's wrong with it?
there's no specific rule against bringing a victorian piston powered whaling gun onto the cruise...
but bascially it's a big fucking no no mate, you're lucky we're still letting you on
welcome onboard we will shortly be departing for the breeding waters of the humpback whale
if we get a bloody move on we might catch some foreplay
I've had enough of this shit, I'm off to check the lifeboats
SECONDS LATER...
I LIKE TO MOVE I
isn't that Alan's music I can hear?

I LIKE TO MOVE IT MOVE IT
SUDDENLY...
FUCKING ARSEHOLES
looks like the cunts lassoed the top deck
this is your captain speaking, get off the fucking boat we're going down
I LIKE TO MOVE IT MOVE IT
SCREEK
CRUNCH

come back Alan you wanker!
thank fuck we're only 50 foot from the harbour
you alright with that yeah?

so Alan how was the cruise?
HOMEOPATH
I didn't like the layout of my cabin
well Alan I hope you weren't afraid to shift it round a bit, it's very important to feel comfortable in your surroundings

work

I'm applying to go on The Appprentice next year,
can you give me a reference confirming that I'm capable
of bollocksing up really basic tasks to a very high standard

BLOG LAUREATE

thoughts to commemorate the recent television programme 60 minute makeover with Claire Sweeney

Sweeney trotting up and down the stairs,
like a scouse shire horse in a tight jumper ☻
only 3 seconds left you still gotta do the kitchen
knock that wall down now!
tik tok, tik tok, fuck me they've done it ☻
there she stands, majestic in victory, give her a mug of tea
while she rests her tits on the mantelpiece. LOL ☻

LIBERTY TAKER

Time To Clear Up The Piss Pots

Experimental Greetings Card no3

Lazy As Fuck Yeah

Experimental Greetings Card no3

Niche Obscenity Investigator

work

First up I'd like to congratulate you on a really professionally produced CV. I see you have a GCSE in quantum physics
yeah? i haven't read it all through yet

cheese&wine
how did the holiday go Gerry?
not good, i pushed some bloke off a cliff

consumer rights

oh fuck it i'll have a four seasons

work

hello is that maintenance? yeah temperature wise I'm ok but i think the noise levels are contravening european guidelines

home~clubber

my mate at airport security's got a nice little sideline going. Your own fully naked body scan printed on the side of a mug, that's next years Christmas presents sorted out.

LIBERTY TAKER

drive-by abuser

considers 'The Hotel'

alright hotel yeah? big building full of people watching porn and fucking each other
electric kettle and a plate of biscuits in every room? it's alright for some innit
had any famous people in? why don't you scrape up some of their carpet hair and sell it
could be anyones though couldn't it
maybe get 'em to sign it or do some sort of forensic test shit on it
they might want paying then, i don't fucking know you work out the small print yeah, see ya

legal longshots

cheese&wine
you might want to turn the heat down in your jacuzzi, i just lobbed up in it

Arsehole Escalator

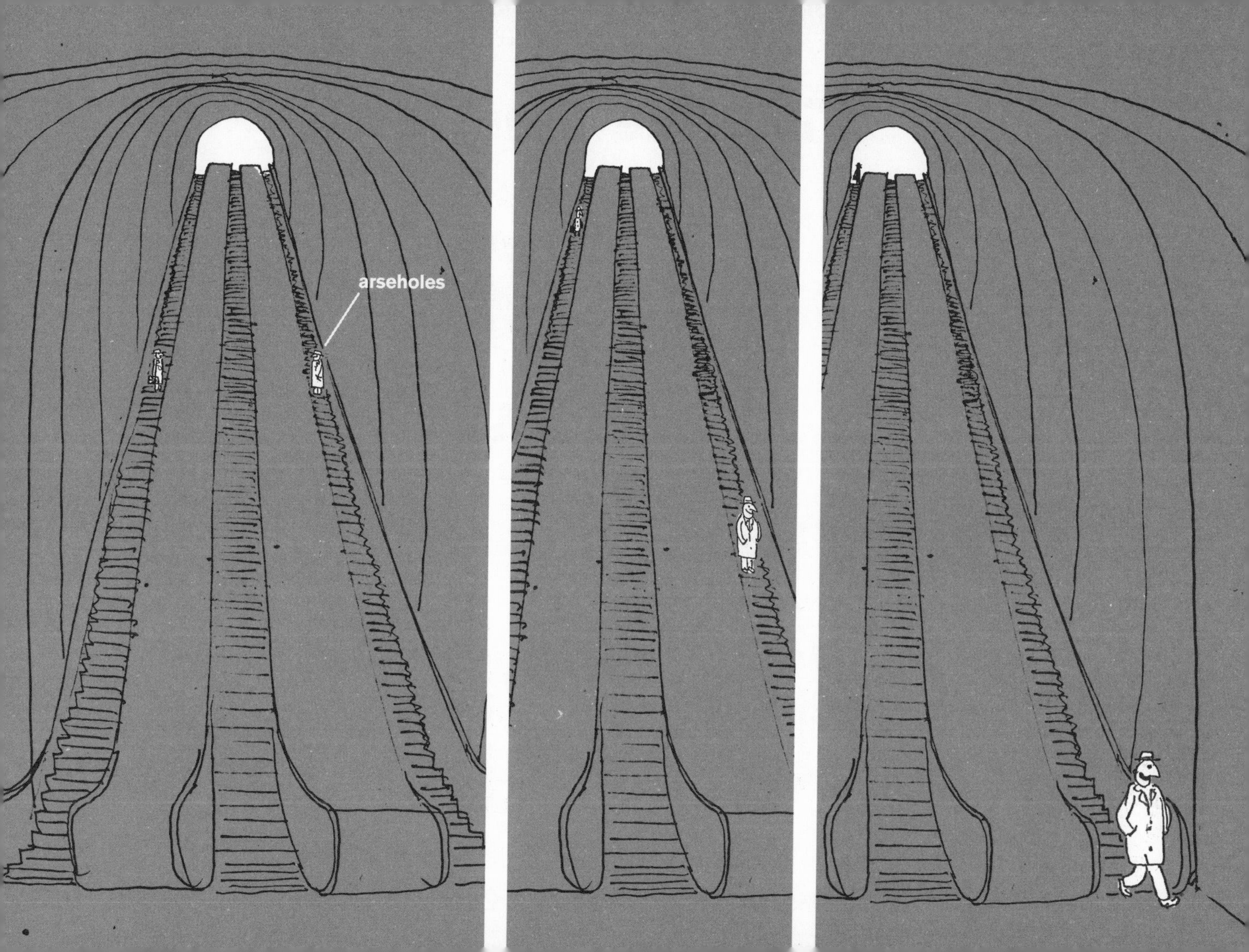
arseholes

Visualize Your Goal

Experimental Greetings Card no5

Mr Tourette

MASTER SIGNWRITER

oh Hello Mr Tourette, I need a new logo for my train company, to distract the passengers from the fact that it's so fucking shit

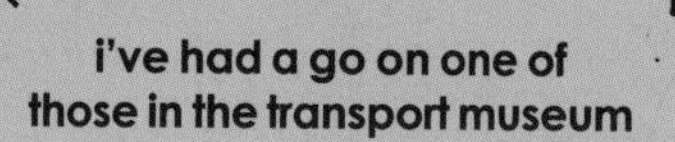

i've had a go on one of those in the transport museum

Later...

we will not tolerate violent or abusive behaviour to our staff, by the way the train on platform 3 is fucked, cheers

THE CRAWLING SHIT WEASEL WITH BROKEN PISS CUPBOARD

i'm not sure about the font but it's definately in tune with the commuter mood

yeah should buy you enough time to get back in your helicopter

THE FRIENDS OF MODERN TOSS

WE VALUE YOUR PATRONAGE

Richard Milne, Rich Parsons, Matthew Cattee, Dean Hunt, Justin Mason, MATTHIEU ROLLAND, Alice and Laurie O'Connor, Cliff Bambridge, Lee Martindale, Elton Lam, Marcella Eaton, David "gamingdave" Robinson, Simon "Big Daddy vee" van Os, Sharon Trickett, Owen 'Double R' Evans, Thomas 'Ball Bag' Crompton, Russell "rusty" Dean, Rach, Ben and The Ikey aka Mrs Mr & Master Tourette, Jamie Keddie, David J A Wood (the), Louise Tait, Peter Griffiths, Graeme Langlands, Corinne 'Sex Bomb' Fulford, Jeri Low Blow, Jeremy "Sense Worldwide" Brown, Dicko, John Kwoka, Steve Potz-Rayner, TomTit Wash? www.kitsch-u-like.com, Sarah Roberts, Nik Margolis, Joe Wright, Andrea Light, Rob Jones, Gareth Barton, Mic Howes, Kyleigh 'on the back of this comic, yeah?' Orlebar, Chris 'buying more shit' Sharman, Gary Wales, Ben Sutcliffe, Jonathan Miles, FlyingDutchman, Christine Kellogg GCSE. Hons, Mankauf, Flubster, Christopher Parry, Patch Hayes, Richard "how old?" Kemp, Justin A, Sarah 'Bizz Wizz' Wright, Thadius Concept, Nathan Walker, Rachel Myburgh, Jenni Cowdy, Nigel 'FFC' Griffiths, Steph Prichard, Su 'Virgin' Davies, Assorted Reays (P,V,S & K), Mark Design, Darren Smith, Andrew Turner, Richard Pedrick, Kiran Khetia, bazzalee, Chris Clay, Sir Leeroy Mullin of Cuntsville, Rob "the Tosser's got all these books" Halloway, m477g8415h & n1(k/3n2, Renata, Craig Smith, Alan Lewis, Olly "What would Sugar do?" Patterson, Adam Merlin James, Christopher Holden, Anna 'See ya round yeh?' Company, Ritchie love Mandy long time, Zoe Richmond-Smith, Alan D Cheyne, Danny Crump, Duncan Cook, Alan Phelan, Jodie 'Got your name a book yeah?' Edgson, Matt RSJ, Luke Miller, Dean J Morbey, George Holt, Claire "Ron" Aldous, Betsy and Corrina, Jon Laming, Mat Eames, Benoist GESLIN, Felicity Reardon, Steve Hayward, Neil Lowden, Sue "ocelot buttonhole" Hayward, Booga, Nick Kenny, Mr and Mrs Sherrersfo, Stephen "Just Friends, Yeah?" Martin, Joe & Sam Wicks, James Nadin, Van Norris, Aled Rogers, Gentleman Joseph & Lamby, Diana Evans, Matt Guy, Ben Gould, charlie cha cha le bona, Ian 'Humpty' Humphreys, hatchend solly, Molly Molloy, ScavType84, Jonny Hall and his magic bongos, Dave, Karen, Lily and Annie High, Robert Dawes, *ROB TAMLIN*, Hayley Heenan, Florence Wylde Raworth, Jim Christian, Tooney, Kieron Smith, ROBERTO, Tigger Burton, Gestreifter Alf, Julia Barton, Kevin McClenaghan, The Stone Twins, James O'Hare, Iain "SHIT CUNT" Wareham, Dan "I HATE JENNA" Augey, Joseph Nation, Anne, Stephen & Eleanor Curran, - MIKRO YEAH? -, Iain "like a BAWSE" Wilson, Ant + Hels + Chibi, Dave Pullig, Kat Chalmers, Happy 2nd Birthday Henry Bruno Russell, yeah!, Paul Thomsen Kirk, DOPSKOP, John Martin, Mike Savage, Ant 'I read it on the shitter' Farmer, Darren Startup, Matthew Carter, Harvey Harvard Powell, Andi Fenner, Tom and Val Raworth, wooley gromit, Ollie W, Paul Cross, Damien Warburton and Domino Woodstock, Matt Lucock, Reverend Ram Rod Tod, Jefrey with one "F" Jefrey, Graff-City.com, Rothko & Serafina, StickyStickster, Kath & Ste, Chowder and the Sqirspies, Miss Lisa Ellen Butcher, DFR, Tony Morley, Ben Winbolt-Lewis, James 'bumhole' Sewell, Katherine Doggrell, Saq Rasul, Pien van Antwerpen, Doctor Benjaminge Williams, big arse sailor with ray pissed, Steven Black, Joseph Millen, Cap'n Billy Firebeard (and wifey), Faye Brimson, Ray McColl, Greg Govier, John the Dick(er), Menelas, Suzanne Curran, Andy 'the dude' P, Anthony and Anna Maude, Liam Franklin, Claire Webber, BlobOfMark, Stuart 'you'll have to be a bit more fucking specific' Wilson, Ross Neary, Mike 'dwards, lil' kels and sam spacey, Ciaran Flynn, Colonel Ross Basford,

Tom Fitzgerald, Mac 10 and the Hogg, George Salmon, Collapse Design, Andy Tough, Meester Bond, Damien Hadley and Amy Carpenter, Simon Hunter, Dave Johnson, Stewart Killala, Niko Guenther, Bombshell Thompson, Rubadubes, Matthew Keen, squirrelboy, Glen Edwards, Scott Hardy, Daniel Jarvis, MIKE AND LAURA, Paul S J Martin, jaime lhas read, Tim Lusher, Lee Barrett, Kathryn & Phil, Bob Pullen, "johnnyapples", Jason Rodger, Neil Coxon, spellnet_terrestrial, Chris Spann, a child rasputin, Sebastian Walker, Samantha Tang, Joseph N Samuel, Niall Gault, Edmund the Wizard, Jos&Sas&Barney&Elliot, Gary Thorogood-Page, a kid called Marni Rimmer yeah!, Richard Oh For God's Sake Get A Grip Paul-Jones, Tom Smith, Happy Birthday Sturtz! Jon Ducker, Jimbo Lightfoot Buddhafella, Ben Golding, Paul Jackman, Peter Gooderham, MATTY WILSON, hot_away@hotmail.com, Maria 'Deadloss' Kikillos, Queen of Cake, Maria 'Deadloss' Kikillos, Queen of Cake, Michael 'Handsy' Blay, Jamie McCall, Gary Hughes, Florence Raworth, Jon Bremner, Ian Gibbonchrist, Graeme Patterson, Alison Walster, Meghan Murphy, Benbenbenbenbenben, Thomas Canning, matt13, Kevin Hill, The Amazing Alison, Kevatronix, Scott Frankling, Lisa Jackson, Kettle, Robin Woodward, Phil Williams, Ramila BW & Catriona KW, Jamie Topham, Imogen Hammond, Stephanie Brown, Agneau Farquhar, David & Helen, Phil & Kate Whaite, Ray Moody, alan Smallwood, Ben Robinson, Lee-Purveyor of Fine Beds-Hawkes, Roberta Fuller, Simon "some sort of cunt" Arnold, Claire Aldous, Rachel Jones, Neil "Tango" Tandy, Snorri Rasmussen, Daniel Waring, Christopher Neilson, Rachel White, Mark Winch, Ben Chadwick, Charles Wander, Victoria O'Malley, Cricko, Vern, Tree+Ham, Mareka Carter, Sam Bott on the Misty Mooring, Ian W, DIABETIC GEZ, Ben Chapman-Yeah!, Roonsa, Charlie Coleman, Adrian Hardwick, Lucy White, Helen Marquis, BW, L Pepper The Hotsteppa, Colin Polly, Matt Hook representing Wales, The Bakers-Flax-StheD-Moles, David Brown, Justine Griffiths, Matt Payne, Mickey Rose, Alexander Prineas, Fraser Clarke, Charlotte Pearson, Perter Halliwell, Allison Flynn, Steve Pape, Rossy & Kate-pac, Steven Rye, Sarah Watt, Denis & Anne faith Hook aka Mr and Mrs DON! Richard Bate, Mike Parkin, Andy, Sharon + Faye, Royllrus, phil_elsie&jack, Big 'ol orange coat & GiFi, Paul Gregson, Jules Scott, Jake Flavell..... and Kate, Alix Jackson, Tim Havard, Nick Beneke, chris p, Alistair Reith, Jonathan Sear, Reading this McWhirr? Robert Dawes, Andy Walker, Grumpy Graham Naylor, Dolly Dixon, Garrison "Hot Dinkle" Maisey, Steve E-Waring, the boy Crump, Stephen Farley, Jamie Macvie, Mike Currie, Simon Harris, Mouse & Fox, Nicola Newman, Dr Rachel Tinker, Neil Maclean, Darran Curant, Euan Tulloch, Georgia Butler, Qwoocy, Alan (Smith), Steve Wrench yeah? Jon & Natasha Fielden, Andy Lockwood, Stu "The Gooch" Goode, ***BENJAMIN JOHN HOLT***, Damian 'Cheese Man' Martin, Paola McClure, Ben Lindsay, Joanna Wiegman, Lucas Williams, Julien Winfield, Niven, Robert Mesure, Alex Fraser, Michael Hurn, Andrew Carlin, Richard H. Morris, Chris Cheetham, Tom Dussek, Daniel Cavanagh, Sam Gillespie, Rob Ford, Jake "Bakes a mean flapjack" Williams, Vive la République, Deborah Sibbald, Mark Maplethorpe, Charlie MacDonald, Lucy Purdon, Rich & Cath, Andy 'DVN & Stratt fucker' Fernandez, Adam Wilkinson, Jonathan D King, Liam "Bwarlhead" Radley, Tom White, Dominic 'Francois' O'Malley, Hywel Roberts, Charley Pearson, Damian 'Jesus' Lodge, Pavel Stasek, Our Mand Bruzon, @judgedewie, jonathan"synth"stephens, James (Blobbs) Roberts, Dr Ian Palmer, Gavin Mackie,

Jenni Mellis, Laird Ainslie, Ross 'fuck work' Macwaters, Daz & Kate, Marmot, Paul David Buckley, gilpin, Oli Kenny, mendi, James A. McMurray, Charles Hutton, Ian Funnell, Chas Barrett, Sam 'Mule' Grantham, Stephanie Tait, Edward 'Oggie' Pritt, Jon Private Taylor, Robin Fulford, Martin HARRONZ Palk, Adam Cooper, Rennik 2000, Stuart Collins, Rob Borland, Liam Clarke, Tom "Rope Boy" Parker, David Peacock, Tim Roberts, Grace Shenanigans Hannigan, Colm Nolan, Richard Black, JJ, Zoe and Little Jack Mercer, Glynn Clarkson, Gareth Germer, Jonathan Mason, Turd polisher yeah?, Adrian Brett, Chris Naughton, Matt Sheehan, Gemma McAvoy, Benjamin P Howell, Roo '17 Ohn Kosak' Lewis, Dylan James, Lucy Hunter, MIKE STAFFORD IN CAPITALS, Lynsey Campbell, Alan Campbell Colin McAlinden, Jimmy Tweedie, Simon TAAFFE, deps & ju "Having a pint, yeah?", Love Bird & Darling, Jolan Pedersen, Deano Gibson, Annie Bellamy, Ricardo Bellchez, David 'some sorta cunt?' Harkin, John R King, Garry&Jenna yeah?, Steve Burns, Steven Kehoe, Elizabeth Bond, Diana Walker, yoko oh!no of RockB, Credence "About Fucking Time" Cole 27/02/10, Sarah "I'll cut ya" Pipes, thebot, robd, Chris K. Willie, Christine Cowin, Meekog the Wrecking Ball, Miguel Martin, Brian Hayes, Helen & Simon Lindley, Neil Overett, Barrie Hemsley, Rebekah Lord, Lewis Hill, Ben Finn, James "name in a fucking book" Clarke, Hatstand Walsh, Jon Mawson, Chris Spark, Aaron Joyce, Ladies Choice (allegedly), Fat boy Masters, Adrian Hardwick, Neil "Edmund Slackbladder" Parker, Matthew Bailey, Frankie Chuckle, Edwardomundo Gillespie, Jode Mayhew, Steve Matthews, FRAN MOORE, The Brothers Cloke, Ricardo Racoon (he loves Joanna), Fay "make mine a big one" Mahdi, mark_13, Russell Tweed, Booze face, Andy Fucking Upton, Colonel Ross Basford DFC, AFC, (ret), Brian Kavanagh yeah, Andy displaced McDonnell, Rob Crespo, SIMON DAVIES, Nick Mackeson-Smith, Kevin Doherty, Andrew Scrivener, Nick Parker-Groom, Dave Littlechild, Sara Faulkner, Jonny "Shithouse" Moore, Charles Whitehouse-cums-Wildly, Craig Pakes, Simon Ozzy Osment, Dave Kirkwood, Paul Roberts, Kate Russell, Mike, Tom Rambo Farmer, Donna Murrell, David Watkins, Miho.O, FROGLEGS, Doug Huggins, Leah Borromeo, SwissToby, Moktok, Mark Griffin, BRAINS LOVES TIGGA, Hannah Cotton, Nathan 'nudge' Allison, Neon & PLF, Steve Williams, Michael Pearman, Neil Cocklin, Al&Marc, Kate Whitty, Carlos Spicy Weiner, Illicit Still Productions, Nikki Chowdry, crossbones, Aran, Adam "Stratfink" Stratton, Gregor Gnasher Rogers, BairstowDTD, Paul Moulton, Colin Day, Lord Harry, Toey Ifsun, Terry Chwowa, Alison Crinion, Rory Gilmore, David Julie and Fran, Secret Pie, Mr Chib, Skilly, Ed Tolley, Toby "this is my kind of humour" Marshall, BUBBA, DJ Wiggles, Alexander Nicholas, Oli Harrex, Dean (if you think I'm gonna mention you rob you can fuck off and buy your own book) Chant, TR 'another pointless entry just to show Abby it really is printed' McGowran, Andy, Lois&Koji, Molly the White Swan Pub Dog, Nick Roseblade, Mike Lee, Ed Shaw, Ed Shaw, Graeme Ian Walker, Bruce & Margaret, Tommy D, Stephen Pinner, Christopher Tong, ANDREW BARLOW, Relims, Didnelps, Danny Vibeside, Russell Graham, Elisa Parish, Ian Cottingham, Aron Okines, ADDIE JAY WHAT THE FUCK (myspace.com/addiejay), Mr MJM, Philly Amory, Paul Allen, Martyn James, Bronyck Horrible Stokes, DARREN HOPTON YEAH, OD=OK, Paula Stubbs, Tiffin Mc Spazmo A.K.A. Aaron Taylor-Cotter, thatjonallen, hiimthom, Debbie Smith, Pauly & Sarah Surridge